SING FOR YOUR LI

44 songs to change the world

chosen by Sandra Kerr

A & C Black • London

MUSIC EDITION ISBN 7136–5546–1
Also available: Melody edition (7136–5662–X)
Cassette (7136–5664–6)

Cover photo by Andrew Wiard (Report)
Illustrations by Samapatti
Musical arrangements by Brian Hunt and Peter Nickol

Contents

Guitar chords

Building a dream

The summer was long

The world's ill divided

It's life we're here for

First published 1987 by A & C Black (Publishers) Ltd,
35 Bedford Row, London WC1R 4JH
© 1987 A & C Black (Publishers) Ltd

Printed in Great Britain by Hollen Street Press Ltd,
Slough, Berks

Guitar chords

x   string should not be sounded
o   open string
⌒   "barre" – two or more strings held down by one finger

C

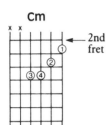

C   C7   Cm

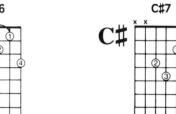

Cm7   C+/aug   C7−9   Cm6

C#

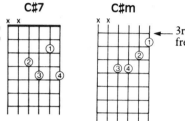

C#7   C#m

D

D   D7   Dm   Dm7   D6   D7−5   D11   D+/aug   Dm6   Dm9

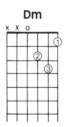
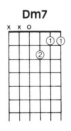
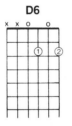
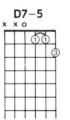
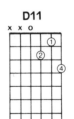
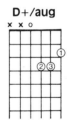
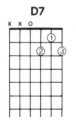

E♭

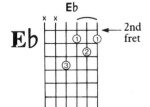

E♭ — 2nd fret

E

E   E7   Em   Em7   E9   Esus   E7sus   Edim

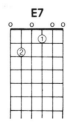

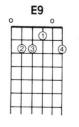
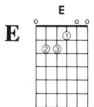

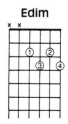

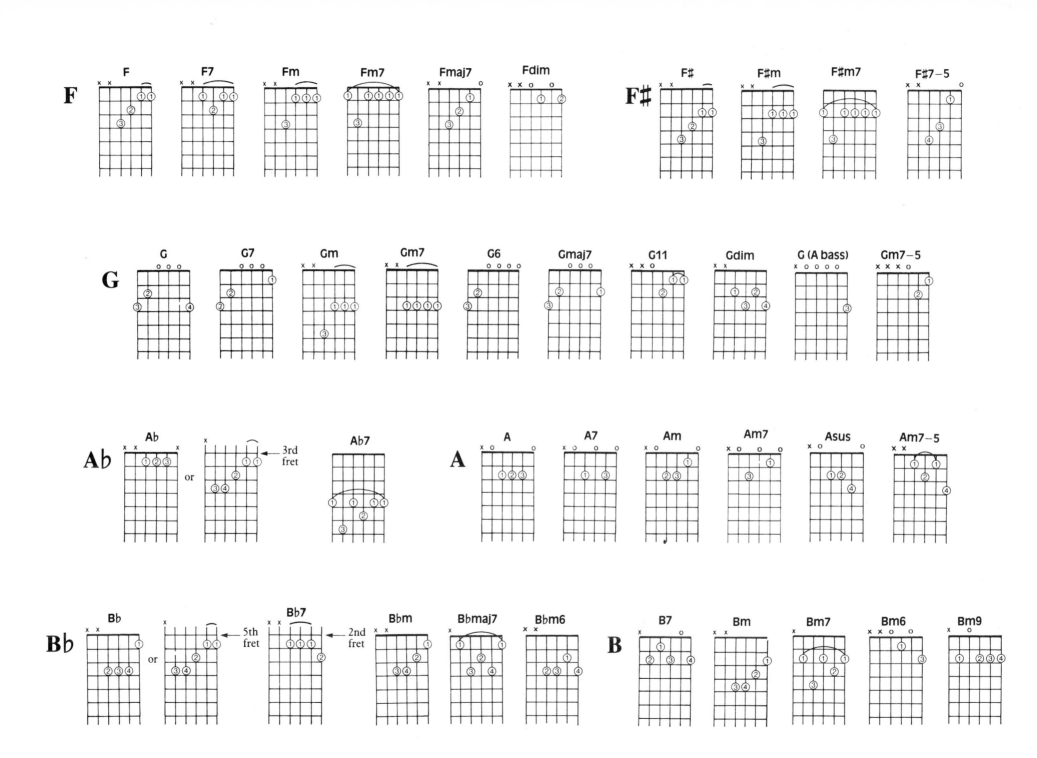

1 History lesson

Leon Rosselson

1. His-to-ry les-son, it's time to re-mem-ber, Time to re-mem-ber the deeds of the great.

Please pay at-ten-tion, don't let your minds wan-der. Day-dreams and play-time can wait. Black the

min-nows that swarm in the wa-ter, White the but-ter-fly flits in the sun,

Red___ the blos-som and pink the mag-nol-ia, His-to-ry les-son's be-gun.___

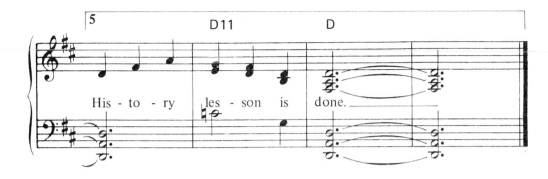

His-to-ry les-son is done.

In form the song 'History Lesson' mirrors Henry Reed's poem 'Naming of Parts', though its content is closer to this poem by Bertolt Brecht:

A WORKER READS HISTORY

Who built the seven gates of Thebes?
The books are filled with the names of kings.
Was it kings who hauled the craggy blocks of stone?
And Babylon, so many times destroyed,
Who built the city up each time? In which of Lima's houses,
That city glittering with gold, lived those who built it?
In the evening when the Chinese wall was finished
Where did the masons go? Imperial Rome
Is full of arcs of triumph. Who reared them up? Over whom
Did the Caesars triumph? Byzantium lives in song,
Were all her dwellings palaces? And even in Atlantis of the legend
The night the sea rushed in,
The drowning men still bellowed for their slaves.

Young Alexander conquered India.
He alone?
Caesar beat the Gauls.
Was there not even a cook in his army?
Philip of Spain wept as his fleet
Was sunk and destroyed. Were there no other tears?
Frederick the Great triumphed in the Seven Years War. Who
Triumphed with him?

Each page a victory,
At whose expense the victory ball?
Every ten years a great man,
Who paid the piper?

So many particulars.
So many questions.

2 Joan of Arc ended up as a cinder,
   Henry the Eighth did for two of his wives.
   Wish I could dive in the pond where the ducks are,
   Having the time of their lives.
       Red the blood on the axe of the headsman,
       Black the stake and the bodies that burn,
       White the face of the priest and the hangman,
       These are the facts you must learn.

3 Pitt paid a packet to patch out an empire,
   Drake bowled the Spaniards out, very first ball.
   Just want to lie in the sun by the water,
   Down where the rushes grow tall.
       Red the lines of Wellington's army,
       White the ensign where Nelson held sway,
       Crimson the Cavalry Marlborough commanded,
       History's heroes are they.

4 Which scrap of paper began the big bundle?
   Which umbrella brought peace in our time?
   Questions and answers dissolve in the sunshine,
   Wait for the school bell to chime.
       Green the gas as it gutters the trenches,
       Black the smell of the smoke from a gun,
       White the pain of a bombshell exploding,
       History lesson's begun.

5 History lesson, please try to remember,
   Try to remember the deeds of the great;
   Theirs was the power, the glory, the honour,
   They were the chosen of fate.
       Black the minnows that swarm in the water,
       White the butterfly flits in the sun,
       Red the blossom and pink the magnolia,
       History lesson is done.

2 Factory girl

N American (c1830)

1 No more shall I work in the factory,
   Greasy up my clothes;
   No more shall I work in the factory
   With splinters in my toes.

        Pity me my darling,
        Pity me, I say.
        Pity me my darling
        And carry my blues away.

2 No more shall I put my bonnet on,
   Hasten to the mill;
   While all the girls are working hard
   I'll be sitting still.

        Pity me my darling . . .

3 No more shall I hear the drummer wheels
   Rolling o'er my head;
   When other girls are hard at work
   I'll be home in bed.

        Pity me my darling . . .

4 No more shall I lay my bobbins up,
   No more take them down;
   No more I'll sweep the dirty floor
   For I'll be out of town.

        Pity me my darling . . .

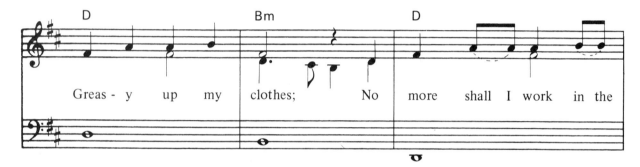

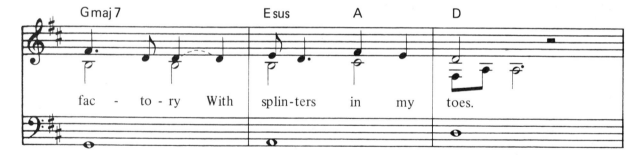

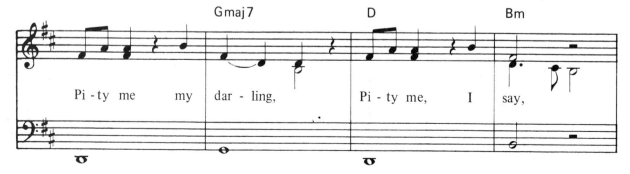

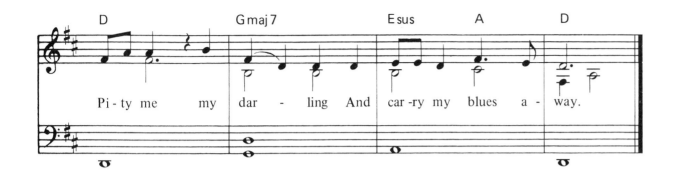

Pi - ty me my dar - ling And car -ry my blues a - way.

5 It's soon you'll see me marrying
   A handsome little man;
   It's then I'll say to you factory girls
   'Come and see me when you can'.

   Pity me my darling...

GIRLS IN A FACTORY

Seated in rows at the machines
Their heads are bent; the tacking needle
Stitches along the hours, along the seams.

What thoughts follow the needle
Over the fields of cloth,
Stitching into the seams
Perhaps a scarlet thread of love,
A daisy-chain of dreams?

Denis Glover

ROSHINI KEMPADOO/FORMAT

3 I don't want your millions, Mister

words: Jim Garland
music: traditional

1 I don't want your millions, Mister,
  I don't want your diamond ring,
  All I want is the right to live, Mister,
  Give me back my job again.

2 I don't want your Rolls-Royce, Mister,
  I don't want your pleasure yacht,
  All I want is food for my babies,
  Give to me my old job back.

3 We worked hard to build this country,
  While you had a life of ease,
  Now you've stole all that we built, Mister,
  Now our children starve and freeze.

4 Think me dumb if you wish, Mister,
  Call me green, or blue or red;
  This one thing I sure know, Mister,
  Hungry babies must be fed.

SHEILA GRAY/FORMAT

4 Brother can you spare a dime?

words: E Y Harburg
music: Jay Gorney

They used to tell me I was build-ing a dream,___ And so I fol-lowed the mob,___

When there was earth to plough or guns to bear___ I was al-ways there,___ right on the job.

They used to tell me I was build-ing a dream,___ With peace and glo-ry a-head;_____ Why should

I be stand-ing in line Just wait-ing for bread?

rit.

(Turn over)

-dum.

Half a mil-lion boots went slog-ging through hell, And I was the kid___ with the drum.___

___ Say don't you re-mem-ber, they called me Al___ It was Al___ all the

time. Say don't you re-mem-ber? I'm your pal!___ Bud-dy, can you spare a dime?___

It is only when you lodge in streets where nobody has a job, where getting a job seems about as probable as owning an aeroplane and much less probable than winning fifty pounds in the Football Pool, that you begin to grasp the changes that are being worked in our civilisation.

George Orwell 'The Road to Wigan Pier' (1937)

5 Pie in the sky

words: Joe Hill
music: anonymous

1 Long-haired preachers come out every night
   And they tell you what's wrong and what's right;
   When you ask them for something to eat,
   They will answer in voices so sweet:

   You will eat, bye and bye,
   In that glorious land above the sky,
   Work and pray, live on hay,
   You'll get pie in the sky when you die.

2 Oh, the starvation army they play,
   And they sing and they clap and they pray,
   Till they get all your coins on the drum,
   Then they'll tell you when you're on the bum.

   You will eat . . .

3 Holy Rollers and Jumpers come out
   And they holler, they jump and they shout.
   'Give your money to Jesus' they say,
   'He will cure all diseases today.'

   You will eat . . .

4 If you fight hard for children and wife,
   Try to get something good in this life,
   You're a sinner and bad man, they tell,
   When you die you will sure go to Hell.

   You will eat . . .

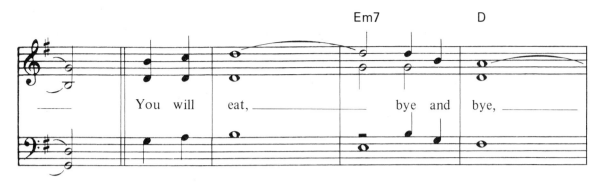

You will   eat, _____   bye   and   bye,

_____   In   that   glor-ious _____   land   a-bove the   sky, _____

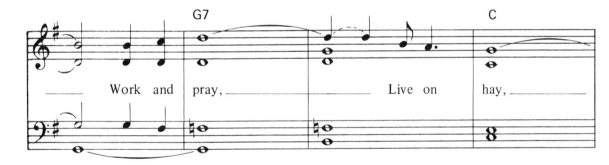

_____   Work   and   pray, _____   Live   on   hay, _____

_____   You'll   get   pie   in   the   sky   when you   die. _____

5   Working men of all countries unite;
    Side by side we for freedom will fight.
    When the world and its wealth we have gained
    To the grafter we'll sing this refrain:

    You will eat, bye and bye,
    When you've learned how to cook and to fry,
    Chop some wood, 'twill do you good,
    And you'll eat in the sweet bye and bye.

Joe Hill moved to the United States from Sweden in the early 1900s. He joined the 'Industrial Workers of the World', a labour movement that strove towards a society run by workers. His songs popularised the aims of the IWW by giving new words to well-known tunes. 'Pie in the sky' is to a hymn tune 'The sweet bye and bye'.

As a disgruntled heckler once said on Tower Hill: 'The trouble with you parsons is that you are everlastingly answering the questions no one is asking'. The accusation may be extravagant, but it contains an element of truth — a concentration on matters which are exclusively 'spiritual' has time and again been the occupational disease of the pulpiteer. All too often the Church has assumed a concern about eternal life on the part of its congregations when, as a matter of bare fact, the cares of this world have rendered such a preoccupation practically impossible.

Donald Soper 'Calling for Action' (1984)

6 Balm in Gilead

Spiritual

There is a balm in Gilead
To make the wounded whole,
There is a balm in Gilead
To heal the sin-sick soul.
(*repeat*)

1 Sometimes I feel discouraged
And think my work in vain,
But then the Holy Spirit
Revives my soul again.

There is a balm in Gilead . . .
(*once only*)

2 Don't ever feel discouraged
Our Father is our friend,
And if you lack the knowledge
He'll not refuse to lend.

There is a balm in Gilead . . .
(*once only*)

3 You may not preach like Peter,
You may not preach like Paul,
But you can tell the story
Of one who died for all.

There is a balm in Gilead . . .
(*once only*)

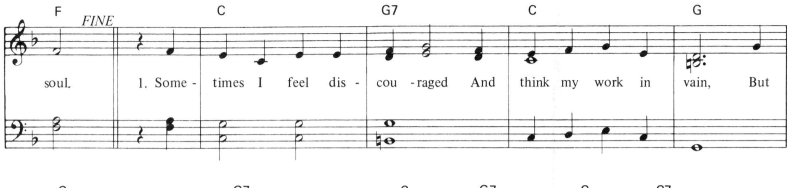

soul. | 1. Some - times I feel dis - cou - raged And think my work in vain, But

then the Ho - ly Spi - rit Re - vives my soul a - gain. There — is a

Gilead was a region by the Jordan of mainly rugged highland, suitable for grazing cattle. It was famous for plentiful supplies of balm, an aromatic spice with healing properties, extracted from bushes. When the prophet Jeremiah foresaw the oppression of Judah's people and their exile in Babylon he asked 'Is there no balm in Gilead?', expressing the utmost despair and the least hope of consolation.

The song 'Balm in Gilead' is based on a Negro spiritual in which Jeremiah's words are echoed by a different people dwelling in a country far from their home, searching for consolation.

When I would comfort myself against sorrow, my heart is faint within me. Behold the voice of the cry of the daughter of my people because of them that dwell in a far country: Is not the Lord in Zion? is not her king in her? Why have they provoked me to anger with their graven images, and with strange vanities? The harvest is past, the summer is ended, and we are not saved. For the hurt of the daughter of my people am I hurt; I am black; astonishment hath taken hold on me. Is there no balm in Gilead; is there no physician there? why then is not the health of the daughter of my people recovered?

The Bible: Jeremiah 9:18–22

7 The mask I wore

Sydney Carter

1 I wore the mask of a baby
(Teddy bear and curly hair)
I wore the mask of a baby
For all the world to see.

2 I wore the mask of a schoolboy
(Bat and ball and cane and all)
I wore the mask of a schoolboy
For all the world to see.

3 I wore the mask of a soldier
(Hold up your head, the sergeant said)
I wore the mask of a soldier
For all the world to see.

4 I wore the mask of a married man
(Goodbye, darling, every morning)
Wore the mask of a married man
For all the world to see.

5 They'll ring that bell for a dead man
The mask I wore I'll wear no more.
Ring that bell for a dead man
You'll never bury me.

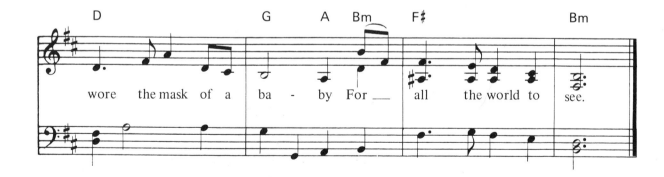

8 She's bought a hat like Princess Marina's

Ray Davies

1. She's bought a hat like Prin-cess Ma - ri - na's To

wear at all her so-cial af - fairs; She wears it when she's clean-ing the win - dows, She

wears it when she's scrub-bing the stairs. But you will ne-ver see her at As - cot, She

9 Turning the clock back

Alex Glasgow

1 My granny tells me she's seen it all before,
And at ninety-four she's seen a thing or two.
She's seen the stockbrokers crying.
And the speculators sighing,
And the millionaires relying
On a war to pull them through.

    And they're turning the clock back
    I can hear me granny say,
    Yes they're turning the clock back
    And the working man will pay.

2 My gran remembers the way it used to be
With Baldwin and MacDonald in the chair.
She fetched the soup from down the kitchen,
Heard the speeches, saw men marching,
Read how Churchill sent the troops in
(Which the papers said was fair).

    And they're turning the clock back
    I can hear me granny say,
    Yes they're turning the clock back
    And the working man will pay.

3 My granny tells me they're at it once again;
The nobs can't get their profits quite as high.
And Tom and Dick and Harry
Have forgotten that they carry
On their shoulders all the parasites
That suck their bodies dry.

-ly-ing On a war to pull them through.

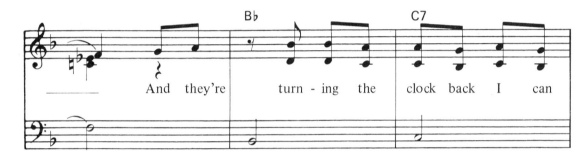

And they're turn-ing the clock back I can

hear me gran-ny say, Yes they're turn-ing the

clock back And the work-ing man will pay.

And they're turning the clock back
I can hear me granny say,
They may call it a Social Contract
But the working man will pay.

4   My granny tells me it's getting very late,
And we've stuck our silly heads down in the sand;
She says she has a nasty feeling
We may very soon be reeling
From the evil-dealing jackboots
As the blackshirts haunt the land.

And they're turning the clock back
I can hear me granny say,
Yes they're turning the clock back
And the working man will pay.

10 Birmingham Sunday

words: Richard Fariña
music: traditional

Birmingham Alabama saw mass demonstrations over the issue of racial integration in 1963. President Kennedy proposed a strong civil rights programme to Congress in June, and in August 200,000 people marched with Martin Luther King to Washington.

In September a bomb exploded in a black church killing four Sunday School girls.

2 That cold autumn morning no eyes saw the sun,
And Addie Mae Collins, her number was one.
At an old Baptist church there was no need to run,
And the choirs kept singing of freedom.

3 The clouds they were grey and the autumn winds blew,
And Denise McNair brought the number to two.
The falcon of death was a creature they knew,
And the choirs kept singing of freedom.

4 The church it was crowded, but no-one could see
That Cynthia Wesley's dark number was three.
Her prayers and her feelings would shame you and me.
And the choirs kept singing of freedom.

5 Then young Carol Robertson entered the door
And the number her killers had given was four.
She asked for a blessing but asked for no more,
And the choirs kept singing of freedom.

6 On Birmingham Sunday a noise shook the ground
And people all over the earth turned around;
For no-one recalled a more cowardly sound.
And the choirs kept singing of freedom.

7 The men in the forest they once asked of me
How many black berries grew in the blue sea.
And I asked them right back with a tear in my eye
How many dark ships in the forest?

8 The Sunday has come and the Sunday has gone.
And I can't do much more than to sing you a song.
I'll sing it so softly, it'll do no-one wrong,
And the choirs keep singing of freedom.

11 Jesus Christ was a man

Woody Guthrie

1 Jesus Christ was a man who travelled through the land,
A carpenter true and brave,
He said to the rich 'Give your goods to the poor'
So they laid Jesus Christ in his grave.

    Yes, Jesus was a man, a carpenter by hand,
    His followers true and brave,
    And a dirty little coward named Judas Iscariot
    He laid Jesus Christ in his grave.

2 The people of the land took Jesus by the hand,
They followed him far and wide,
But he came not to bring them peace but a sword
So they killed Jesus Christ on the sly.

    Yes, Jesus was a man . . .

3 He went to the sick and he went to the poor,
He went to the hungry and lame,
He said that the poor would win this world
So they laid Jesus Christ in his grave.

    Yes, Jesus was a man . . .

4 They nailed Him there to die on a cross in the sky
In the lightning and thunder and rain,
And Judas Iscariot committed suicide
When they laid Jesus Christ in his grave.

    Yes, Jesus was a man . . .

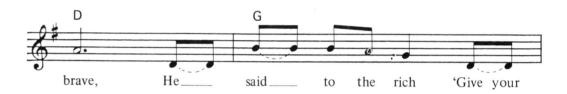

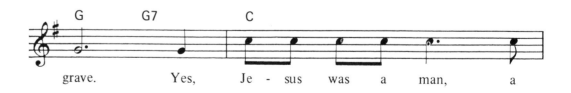

car - pen - ter by hand, His fol - low - ers true and

brave, And a dirt - y lit - tle cow - ard named

Ju - das Is - car - iot, He laid Je - sus Christ in his grave.

5 In this wide wicked world of soldiers and slaves,
Of rich man and poor man and thief,
If Jesus was to preach what he preached in Galilee
They would lay Jesus Christ in his grave.

Yes, Jesus was a man...

6 When the love of the poor shall turn into hate
When the patience of workers gives way
'Twould be better for you rich if you never had been born
For you laid Jesus Christ in his grave.

Yes, Jesus was a man...

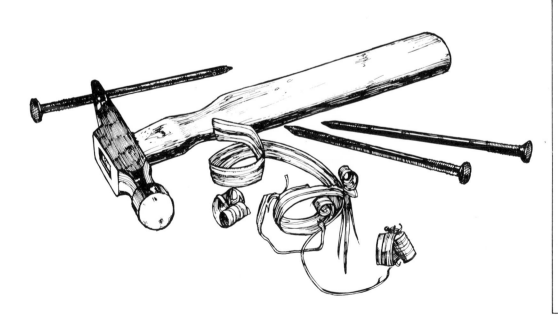

And, behold, one came and said unto him, Good Master, what good thing shall I do, that I may have eternal life? And he said unto him, Why callest thou me good? there is none good but one, that is, God: but if thou wilt enter into life, keep the commandments. He saith unto him, Which? Jesus said, Thou shalt do no murder, Thou shalt not commit adultery, Thou shalt not steal, Thou shalt not bear false witness, Honour thy father and thy mother: and, Thou shalt love thy neighbour as thyself. The young man saith unto him, All these things have I kept from my youth up: what lack I yet? Jesus said unto him, If thou wilt be perfect, go and sell all thou hast, and give to the poor, and thou shalt have treasure in heaven: and come and follow me. But when the young man heard that saying he went away sorrowful: for he had great possessions.

Then Jesus said unto his disciples, Verily I say unto you, That a rich man shall hardly enter into the kingdom of heaven. And again I say unto you, It is easier for a camel to go through the eye of a needle, than for a rich man to enter into the kingdom of God. When his disciples heard it, they were exceedingly amazed, saying, Who then can be saved? But Jesus beheld them, and said unto them, With men this is impossible; but with God all things are possible.

The Bible: Matthew 19:16—26

12 Love is pleasing

Irish

1 O love is pleasing and love is teasing
   And love's a pleasure when first it is new;
   But as love grows older, at length grows colder,
   And fades away like the morning dew.

2 I left my mother, I left my father,
   I left my brother and my sisters too;
   I left my home and my kind relations,
   I left them all for the love of you.

3 I never thought that my love would leave me
   Until one morning when he came in,
   He drew up a chair and sat down beside me
   And then my sorrows they did begin.

4 If I had known before I courted
   That love had been such a killing crime
   I'd have locked my heart in a box of gold
   And tied it up with a silver twine.

5 O love is pleasing and love is teasing
   And love's a pleasure when first it is new;
   But as love grows older, at length grows colder,
   And fades away like the morning dew.

The chord symbols are an alternative harmonisation
which should not be played together with the piano
arrangement.

13 Glass of water

Sydney Carter
(from a Greek melody)

1 The sun is high in the summer sky,
And I must drink or I will die.
Can I have a glass of water?
Can I have a glass of water?
All I want is a glass of water,
All I want is a glass of water.

2 In the doorway where you stand,
Glass of water in your hand,
You are cooler than the water,
You are cooler than the water.
All I want is a glass of water,
All I want is a glass of water.

3 With my eyes I drink you up,
Like the water in the cup,
Drink you like a glass of water,
Drink you like a glass of water.
All I want is a glass of water,
All I want is a glass of water.

4 When the moon is in the sky,
All alone on my bed I lie,
Dreaming of a glass of water,
Dreaming of a glass of water.
All I want is a glass of water,
All I want is a glass of water.

'In Greece when it's hot – really hot – all a
man wants is a glass of water. And to tell a
girl she is like a glass of water is the highest
compliment possible.' *Sydney Carter*

14 Marry or not

Hungarian

1 Marriage is my future!
Single life is ended!
But I have a problem
Choosing my intended.
    Ay ay ay, ay ay ay,
    Who is my intended?
    (*repeat*)

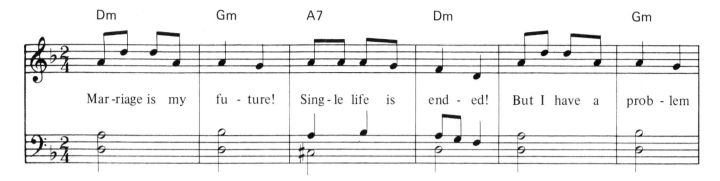

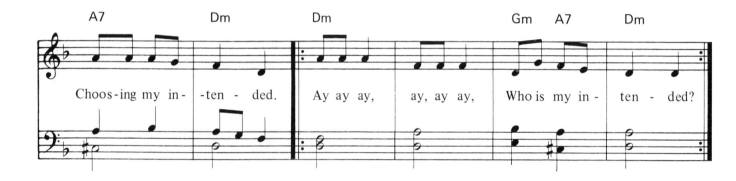

2 I could dance all night with
One who's young and nimble,
But would she be fond of
Frying-pan or thimble?
    Ay ay ay, ay ay ay,
    If she's young and nimble.

3 If my spouse is wealthy
I shall feel protected,
But if she supports me
Will I be respected?
    Ay ay ay, ay ay ay,
    Pride must be protected.

4 If my wife's a poor one
Is it any better?
Doubling my chance of
Ending up a debtor?
    Ay ay ay, ay ay ay,
    Hardly any better!

5 I'd considered marriage
As a consolation.
All it brings is questions,
Worry and vexation.
    Ay ay ay, ay ay ay,
    Where's my consolation?

6 Is my life so cheerless?
Am I just a griper?
I'll postpone my courting
Till the time is riper.
    Ay ay ay, ay ay ay,
    Time will soon be riper!

15 Daughters will you marry?

N American

1 Daughters will you marry?
Yea, father, yea.
Will you marry a farmer?
Nay, father, nay.
A farmer's wife I will not be,
Cleaning out stables is not for me,
Nay, father, nay.

2 Daughters will you marry?
Yea, father, yea.
Will you marry a doctor?
Nay, father, nay.
A doctor's wife I will not be,
Torturing people is not for me,
Nay, father, nay.

3 Daughters will you marry?
Yea, father, yea.
Will you marry a teacher?
Nay, father, nay.
A teacher's wife I will not be,
Punishing children is not for me.
Nay, father, nay.

4 Daughters will you marry?
Yea, father, yea.
Will you marry a lawyer?
Nay, father, nay.
A lawyer's wife I will not be,
Cheating people is not for me,
Nay, father, nay.

5 Daughters will you marry?
Yea, father, yea.
Will you marry a fiddler?
Yea, father, yea.
I'd like to be a fiddler's wife,
Singing and dancing all of my life,
Yea, father, yea.

16 If I was with a woman

words: Ian Dury
music: Chaz Jankel

1. If I was with a wo-man She'd won-der what was happ-'ning ___ Lit-tle things would slow-ly go as-
(3.) I was with a wo-man I'd ne-ver ask her quest-ions, But if she did not want me to, I

- kew. If I was with a wo-man I'd make her quite un-hap-py, Es-pec-ially when she did not want me
would. If I was with a wo-man I'd of-fer my in-dif-f'rence And make quite sure she ne-ver un-der

to. 2. If I was with a wo-man I'd make be-lieve I loved her ___ All the time I would not like her
stood. 4. If I was with a wo-man I'd threat-en to un-load her ___ Ev-'ry time she asked me to ex-
5. I've been with a wo-man, she took a-way my spi-rit. No wo-man's com-ing close to me a-

17 The golden peacock

Jewish folk song

1 The golden peacock, she flew to greet me
Far across the deep blue sea,
Far across the deep blue sea.
Did my dear mother send you here,
Is she thinking now of me?
Did my dear mother send you here,
Is she thinking now of me?

2 The golden peacock, she came to greet me
Far across the great wide water . . .
Was my dear father thinking of me,
Of the sadness of his daughter . . . ?

3 The peacock flew through distant kingdoms
Over fields so bare and lonely . . .
Where there fell but a single plume,
One golden feather only . . .

4 How lovely is a flying peacock!
One fine plume is but a feather . . .
Must we live now as people apart
Or as family together . . . ?

5 How sad it is, my dearest mother,
For a fish to want for water . . .
So it is in a stranger's home
For one who is your daughter . . .

6 How sad it is, my golden peacock,
To be taken from your nest . . .
So it is in the home of my in-laws,
An uninvited guest . . .

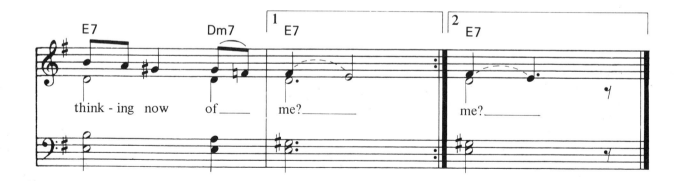

18 Khayana

1 How could my father
   Give me away to this far land?
   Nevermore asking or caring
   Whether I live or die.

2 Daughter and mother
   Met and embraced at the pond-side
   Silently weeping together,
   Filling the pond with tears.

3 At the mill working,
   Hearing the unceasing grinding;
   Mother-in-law will be scolding,
   Scolding until I die.

Ma - rey te ba - pey par - a - desh dik - a - ri

did - hi. _____ Far - i kha - ba - ra na

lid - hi Mu - yee key ji - va - ti.

'Khayana' is the name of a type of 3 line poem. The three verses given here are actually translations of separate poems, the first corresponding to the Gujarati words printed under the music.

Khayanas are often sung by girls as they sit on the long swings which hang from the roofs in Gujarati households, or sometimes as they grind rice.

'The golden peacock' and 'Khayana' come from different cultures but speak of arranged marriage in the same terms.

19 Family secret

Mark Bunyan

1. There they sit, my mum and dad — Mum's feel-ing poor-ly, her va-ri-cose
2. Mum says 'Dad — make us some tea And bring in the bis-cuits'. Says Dad 'No, Vi,

veins___ are bad. And on the set-tee sits Dad's sis-ter
leave it to me'. And Mum___ says 'Well, Vi, how's things with

Vi, Who's watch-ing the tel-ly and wish-ing she had-n't come by.___
you? My-self I'm ex-haust-ed, with kids there's so much to do.___

'Cause Dad said 'Vi's a bun-dle of nerves, we must ask her round to
Of course, you would-n't know what it's like to have kids a-round the

tea'. And Mum said 'Please your-self — she's your sis-ter, but odd if
house. But then, a wo-man's job is her fam-'ly, so I can't

you ask me'. And Dad's___ thoughts turn,___ as of-ten be-fore, To
real-ly grouse. Our Sha-ron's en-gaged, she'll be mar-ried in May, Just

20 Must I be bound?

traditional

1 Must I be bound and you go free?
   Must I love one who ne'er loved me?
   Why should I act such a childish part
   To love a lad who will break my heart?

2 The first thing that my lad gave me
   It was a cap well-lined with lead;
   The longer that I wore that cap
   It grew the heavier on my head.

3 And next he brought me a gown to wear
   With sorrow lined and stitched with fear;
   And the drink he gave me was bitter gall
   And the blows he gave me were worse than all.

4 The third thing that my lad gave me
   It was a belt with colours three;
   The first was sorrow, the next was shame,
   And last of all sad misery.

5 But I shall gain my liberty
   And I shall climb a higher tree
   And I shall find a richer nest
   And be with one I may love best.

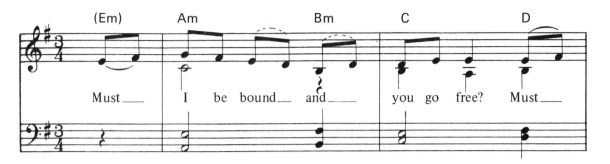

21 Single girl

N American

1 When I was single I went dressed so fine,
   Now I am married, go ragged all the time.
      Lord, I wish I was a single girl again.
      Lord, I wish I was a single girl again.

2 When I was single, ate biscuits and pie,
   Now I am married, eat cornbread or die.
      Lord, I wish I was a single girl again . . .

3 Dishes to wash and spring to go to,
   Now I am married I've everything to do.
      Lord, I wish I was a single girl again . . .

4 When I was single my shoes used to creak,
   Now I am married, well, all they do is leak.
      Lord, I wish I was a single girl again . . .

5 Two little children lying in the bed,
   Both of them hungry and can't hold up their heads.
      Lord, I wish I was a single girl again . . .

6 Wash them and dress them and send them to school,
   'Long comes that drunkard and calls them a fool.
      Lord, I wish I was a single girl again . . .

7 When I was single, marrying was my crave,
   Now I am married I'm troubled to my grave.
      Lord, I wish I was a single girl again . . .

22 Lullaby for a very new baby

Peggy Seeger

1. Oh, the sum-mer was long and the au-tumn too,____ Walk-ing slow and wear-y, Till the win-ter____ part-ed me and___ you, Hush-a-bye, my dear-ie. dear-ie.

2 When the time was come and the time was gone,
   They laid you down so near me,
   And together we slept the whole night long,
   Hushabye, my dearie.

3 But my back is broke and my belly sore,
   Your daddy can't come near me,
   And it's up all night to walk the floor
   Hushabye, my dearie.

4 Though you keep me waking night and day
   And your crying makes me weary,
   You're as welcome as a flower in May,
   Hushabye, my dearie.

5 My darling girl, the world is wide,
   I know it's going to fear me
   To set you floating on the tide
   Hushabye, my dearie.

when you rest
we listen for ticks of breath
study   curved coves inside your ear
folds at your neck   like smooth, loose linen
when you stir
rehearsing each expression
flexing the length of this arm, that leg
you rock the routines of our house
spun   head over heels   by a baby's thumb

from 'Journey to a Birth' by Robert Hamberger

23 Jenny Bell

Mahala Nice

1 Just sixteen was Jenny Bell,
   Jenny, Jenny Bell,
   The story of Jenny I'm going to tell,
   Ah, poor Jenny Bell.

2 Just sixteen and unafraid,
   Jenny, Jenny Bell,
   And all her love, she gave it away,
   Ah, poor Jenny Bell.

3 O mother, O mother, I'm going away . . .
   Down to London I'm going to stay . . .

4 She worked in a shop in Market Street . . .
   Eight hours a day upon her feet . . .

5 And every night she sat alone . . .
   In her room in Marylebone . . .

6 One night the pain was fierce and wild . . .
   She knew it was time to bear her child . . .

7 Down to the hospital Jenny went . . .
   They took her in, for she was spent . . .

8 She smiled when first she saw her son . . .
   Then wept to think what she had done . . .

9 She kissed his hands, his cheek and brow . .
   And away for adoption he did go . . .

10 So Jenny Bell gave up her son . . .
   She never had another one . . .

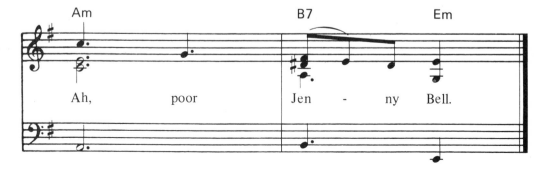

24 I remember Christmas

Sam Richards

1 I remember Christmas,
  Yes I do.
  I remember Christmas,
  How about you?
  I remember Christmas
  As I sit and think;
  Dad was round the boozer,
  Mum at the kitchen sink.

2 I remember Christmas,
  Long ago.
  I remember Christmas,
  Fairy snow.
  Milk of human kindness
  There in every cup;
  When we'd swigged it down
  Then Mum washed up.

3 I remember Christmas
  In my heart.
  Slept through Lizzie's message,
  Heard the chart.
  And when it was finished,
  How nice, we all said;
  We all enjoyed the party –
  Mum was asleep in bed.

25 The work o' the weavers

David Shaw

1. We're all met to-geth-er to sit and to crack With glas-ses in our hands and our wark up-on our back; And there's no trade a-mong us that can eith-er mend or mak But what wears the wark o' the weav - ers. If it was-na for the weav - ers, what would we do? We would-na have cloth made out of our wool; We would-na have a

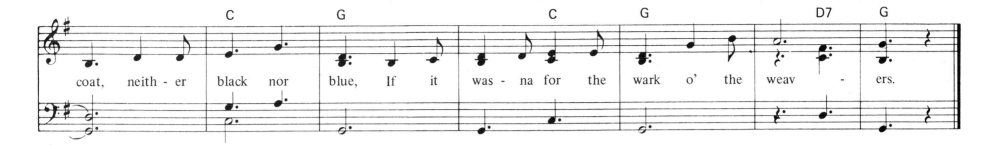

coat, neith-er black nor blue, If it was-na for the wark o' the weav - ers.

2 The hiremen they mock us and they crack aye aboot's.
   They say that we are thin-faced, bleached-like cloots;
   But yet for all their mockery they canna do withoot's,
   No they canna want the wark o' the weavers.

   If it was-na for the weavers...

3 There's sailors and soldiers, we ken they're so bold,
   But if they had no clothes, faith, they could-na fight for cold;
   The high, the low, the rich, the poor, a'body young and old,
   They all need the wark o' the weavers.

   If it was-na for the weavers...

4 Our wrights and our slaters and glaziers and all,
   Our doctors and our ministers and them that live by law;
   Our friends in South America, though them we never saw –
   But we ken they wear the wark o' the weavers.

   If it was-na for the weavers...

5 There's folk independent of other tradesmen's wark
   For women need no barber and dykers need no clerk;
   But none of them can do without a coat or a sark
   Which must be the wark o' some weaver.

   If it was-na for the weavers...

6 So weaving's a trade that can never fail
   As long as we need ae cloot to keep another hale;
   So let's all be merry o'er a bicker o' good ale
   And we'll drink to the wark o' the weavers.

   If it was-na for the weavers...

This song was written by David Shaw of Forfar, a hand loom weaver who sang at Chartist meetings in the 1840s. It has been passed on (and adapted) by oral tradition.

Here are English translations of the Scots expressions:

crack	gossip (or boast)
mak	make
wark	work
hiremen	farmworkers
crack aye aboot's	always talk about us
bleached-like cloots	bleached-out cloths
a'body	everybody
dyker	builder of dykes
sark	shirt or blouse
ae cloot to keep another hale	one piece of cloth to patch another
bicker	beaker

26 The farmer is the man

N American

1 When the farmer comes to town
  With his wagon broken down,
  Oh, the farmer is the man who feeds them all.
  If you'll only look and see,
  I am sure you will agree
  That the farmer is the man who feeds them all.

  The farmer is the man,
  The farmer is the man,
  Lives on credit till the fall;
  Then they take him by the hand
  And they lead him from the land
  And the middleman's the man who gets it all.

2 When the lawyer hangs around
  While the butcher cuts a pound,
  Oh, the farmer is the man who feeds them all.
  And the preacher and the cook
  Go a-strolling by the brook,
  Oh, the farmer is the man who feeds them all.

  The farmer is the man,
  The farmer is the man,
  Lives on credit till the fall;
  With the interest rate so high
  It's a wonder he don't die,
  For the mortgage man's the man who gets it all.

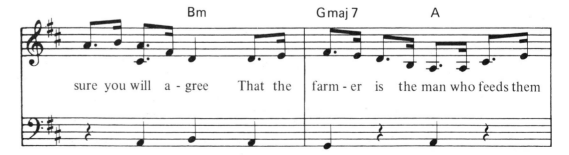

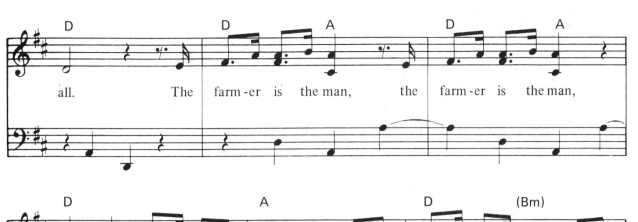

all. The farm-er is the man, the farm-er is the man,

Lives on cre-dit till the fall; Then they take him by the hand And they

lead him from the land And the mid-dle man's the man who gets it all.

3 When the banker says he's broke,
And the merchant's up in smoke,
They forget that it's the farmer
   feeds them all.
It would put them to the test
If the farmer took a rest,
They would know that it's the farmer
   feeds them all.

The farmer is the man,
The farmer is the man,
Lives on credit till the fall;
And his pants are wearing thin,
His condition is a sin,
He's forgot that he's the man
   who feeds them all.

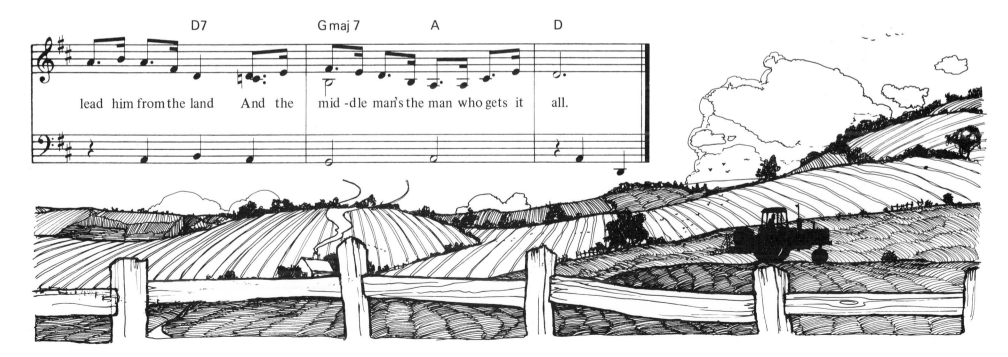

27 Hanging on the old barbed wire

Soldiers' song from WW1

1 If you want to find the General I know where he is,
I know where he is, I know where he is.
If you want to find the General I know where he is,
He's pinning another medal on his chest.
I saw him, I saw him,
Pinning another medal on his chest,
I saw him pinning another medal on his chest.

2 If you want to find the Colonel I know where he is,
I know where he is, I know where he is.
If you want to find the Colonel I know where he is,
He's sitting in comfort stuffing his bloody gut.
I saw him, I saw him,
Sitting in comfort stuffing his bloody gut,
I saw him sitting in comfort stuffing his bloody gut.

3 If you want to find the Major ...
... he's home again on seven days' leave ...

4 If you want to find the Sergeant ...
... he's drinking all the company rum ...

5 If you want to find the Corporal ...
... he's drunk upon the dug-out floor ...

6 If you want to find the Private ...
... he's hanging on the old barbed-wire ...

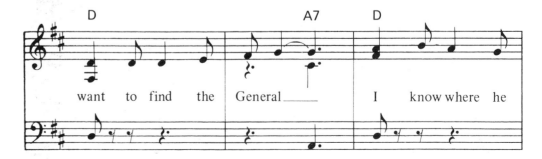

28 The housewife's lament

words: Sarah Price(?)
music: traditional

1 One day I was walking, I heard a complaining,
And saw an old woman the picture of gloom.
She gazed at the mud on her doorstep ('twas raining)
And this was her song as she wielded her broom.

   Oh, life is a toil and love is a trouble,
   Beauty will fade and riches will flee,
   Pleasures they dwindle and prices they double,
   And nothing is as I would wish it to be.

2 There's too much of worriment goes to a bonnet,
There's too much of ironing goes to a shirt.
There's nothing that pays for the time you waste on it,
There's nothing that lasts us but trouble and dirt.

   Oh, life is a toil...

3 In March it is mud, then it's slush in December,
The midsummer breezes are loaded with dust.
In fall the leaves litter, in muddy September
The wallpaper rots and the candlesticks rust.

   Oh, life is a toil...

4 There's worms on the cherries and slugs on the roses,
And ants in the sugar and mice in the pies.
The rubbish of spiders no mortal supposes,
And ravaging roaches and damaging flies.

   Oh, life is a toil...

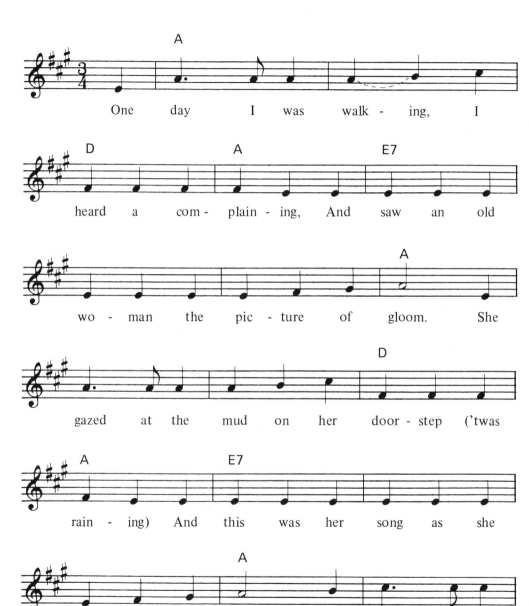

C♯7

toil _____ and love is a trou - ble,

F♯m   **B7**   **E**

Beau - ty will fade _____ and rich - es will

E7   **A**

flee,   Plea -sures they dwin - dle and

D   **A**   **E7**

pri - ces they dou - ble, And no - thing is

A

as I would wish it to be.

5 It's sweeping at six and it's dusting at seven,
It's victuals at eight and it's dishes at nine.
It's potting and panning from ten to eleven,
We scarce finish breakfast, we're ready to dine.

    Oh, life is a toil . . .

6 With grease and with grime from corner to centre
Forever at war and forever alert.
No rest for a day lest the enemy enter,
I spend my whole life in a struggle with dirt.

    Oh, life is a toil . . .

7 Last night in my dreams I was stationed forever
On a far distant rock in the midst of the sea.
My one task of life was a ceaseless endeavour
To brush off the waves as they swept over me.

    Oh, life is a toil . . .

8 Alas, 'twas no dream! Ahead I behold it!
I see I am helpless my fate to avert.
She laid down her broom, her apron she folded,
She lay down and died and was buried in dirt.

    Oh, life is a toil . . .

This song was found in the diary of Sarah Price of Illinois, who lived at the time of the American Civil War.

29 The maintenance engineer

Sandra Kerr

1. One Friday night it hap-pened, some years af-ter we were wed, When my old man came in from work as us-u-al I said, 'Your tea is on the ta-ble,— clean clothes are on the rack, Your bath-'ll soon be rea-dy, I'll come up and scrub your back'. He kissed me ve-ry ten-der-ly and said 'I'll tell you flat, The ser-vice I give my ma-chine ain't half as good as that!'. I said 'I'm

not your lit-tle wo-man, your

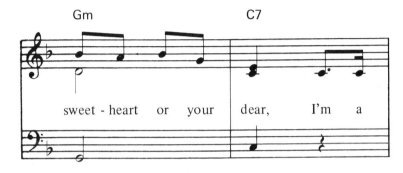

sweet-heart or your dear, I'm a

wage-slave with-out wa-ges, I'm a

main-ten-ance en-gin-eer'.

2 So then we got to talking, I told him how I felt,
How I keep him running just as smooth as some conveyor belt,
For after all it's I'm the one provides the power supply
(He goes just like the clappers on my steak and kidney pie).
My home is just a service station where I sweat and toil,
While he's off to the boozer for his seven pints of oil.

   I said 'I'm not your little woman . . .

3 The truth began to dawn then, how I keep him fit and trim
So the boss can make a nice fat profit out of me and him.
And as a solid union man he got in quite a rage
To think that we're both working hard and getting one man's wage.
I said, 'And what about the part-time packing job I do?
That's three men that I work for, love, my boss, your boss, and you!'.

   I said 'I'm not your little woman . . .

4 He looked a little sheepish and he said 'As from today
The lads and me will see what we can do on equal pay.
Would you like a housewifes' union? Do you think you should be paid
As a cook and as a cleaner, as a nurse and as a maid?'.
I said 'Don't jump the gun, love. If you did your share at home
Perhaps I'd have some time to fight some battles of my own!'.

   I said 'I'm not your little woman . . .

5 I've often heard you tell me how you'll pull the bosses down;
You'll never do it, brother, while you're bossing me around.
Till women join the struggle – married, single, white, and black –
You're fighting with a blindfold and one arm behind your back.
The message has got over for he's realised at last
That power to the sisters must mean to power to the class!

   I said 'I'm not your little woman . . .

30 Poor man's heaven

anonymous

1   Kind friends, gather near, I want you to hear
    A dream that I had last night;
    There's a land o'er the sea for you and for me
    Where we won't have to struggle and fight.
    There's real feather beds where we'll lay our heads,
    In a nice private room for each one.
    There's shoes with soles and pants without holes
    And no work up there to be done.
    In Poor Man's Heaven we'll have our own way
    And we won't have nothing to fear,
    And we'll eat all we please from ham and egg trees
    That grow by the fountains of beer.

2   We won't have to yearn for money to burn
    For we'll own a big money press
    That we'll run at full speed and make all we need,
    And we'll be the guards of the rest.
    The landlords we'll take and tie to a stake
    And we'll make 'em give back all our dough;
    We'll let 'em sweat and learn what they'll get
    When they go to that hot place below.
    In Poor Man's Heaven we'll own our own home
    We won't have to work like a slave;
    But we'll all be so proud to sing right out loud
    The land of the free and the brave.

31 Father Grumble

traditional

★DRONE
The drone could be played on a sustaining instrument such as an electronic organ, or strummed on a string instrument. If the two notes are held down on the piano keyboard they will ring out while the melody is played in the right hand.

1. There was an old man who lived in the wood, As

DRONE *

(continues)

you can plain - ly see. Who said he could do more

work in one day Than his wife could do in three. 'If

that be true' the wo - man said, 'Why then you must al -

-low, That you___ shall do my work for one day While I go drive the plough.'

2 'But you must milk the tiny cow
For fear she should go dry,
And you must feed the little pigs
That are within the sty;
And you must watch the bracket hen
Lest she should lay astray
And you must wind the reel of yarn
That I spun yesterday.'

3 The old woman took the staff in her hand
And went to drive the plough;
The old man took the pail in his hand
And went to milk the cow.
But Tiny hitched and Tiny flitched
And Tiny cocked her nose
And Tiny gave the man such a kick
The blood ran to his toes.

4 And when he had milked the tiny cow
For fear she should go dry,
Why, then he fed the little pigs
That were within the sty.
And then he watched the bracket hen
Lest she should lay astray;
But he forgot the reel of yarn
His wife spun yesterday.

5 He swore by all the stars in heaven
And leaves upon the tree,
His wife could do more work in a day
Than he could do in three.
By all the leaves upon the tree
And all the stars in heaven –
His wife could do more work in a day
Than he could do in seven!

32 Jute mill song

words: Mary Brooksbank
music: Ewan McColl

1 Oh dear me, the mill's going fast,
The poor wee shifters canna get their rest;
Shifting bobbins coarse and fine,
They fairly make you work for your ten-and-nine.

2 Oh dear me, I wish the day was done,
Running up and down the pass is no fun,
Shifting, piecing, spinning, warp, weft and twine,
To feed and clothe my bairnie aff'n ten-and-nine.

3 Oh dear me, the world's ill divided,
Them that work the hardest are the least provided,
But I must bide contented, dark days or fine,
There's no much pleasure living aff'n ten-and-nine.

Jute is a natural fibre which produces material of a quality suitable for bagging or wrapping purposes. Whaling-centre Dundee built an industry on the discovery that whale oil could be mixed with jute fibre to facilitate weaving.

It was the poorest-paid section of the textile industry. Well into the present century women were expected to complete a ten-hour shift before returning to running a home. Mary Brooksbank was a Dundee jute worker who recorded the conditions in her writings.

33 Sleep my baby

Jewish folk song

1 Sleep my baby, I will croon to you,
  I will sing a lullaby,
  And when my child you grow to be a man one day
  You will know all the reasons why.
  And when my child you grow to be a man one day
  You will know all the reasons why.

2 Why our world's divided as it is,
  Why the poor must live in pain,
  Why they must toil upon the land from dawn to dusk
  When the rich come to reap the grain.
  Why they must toil upon the land from dawn to dusk
  When the rich come to reap the grain.

3 Why the finest houses stand so proud
  Side by side upon the hill;
  The man who builds them will not ever live inside,
  No, not he, but the rich man will.
  The man who builds them will not ever live inside,
  No, not he, but the rich man will.

4 Why the poor are sick with overwork,
  Knowing not why they were born
  To live in cellars that are cold and damp and drear,
  There to tremble in clothing torn.
  To live in cellars that are cold and damp and drear,
  There to tremble in clothing torn.

In 1983 54% of Britain's marketable wealth was owned by 10% of the population – that is to say, the wealthiest 10% owned more than the whole of the other 90%.

34 Children of Africa

street song from Soweto

1 We are the children of Africa
And it's for freedom that we're fighting.
We are the children of Africa
And it's for freedom that we're fighting.

A heavy load, a heavy load,
And it will take some real strength.
A heavy load, a heavy load,
And it will take some real strength.

2 We're not afraid of the prison walls,
It's for freedom that we go now.
We're not afraid of the prison walls,
It's for freedom that we go now.

A heavy load...

3 They took our land, they took our homes,
How much longer will they bleed us?
They took our land, they took our homes,
How much longer will they bleed us?

A heavy load...

4 In Soweto they shot us down,
But we will rise up united.
In Soweto they shot us down,
But we will rise up united.

A heavy load...

Soweto is the largest black urban complex in South Africa, having grown out of shanty towns and slums. Many of the 850,000 population travel the 25km to Johannesburg; there is little local work.

In June 1976 black students protested against a government attempt to standardise the language spoken in Soweto high schools. Police replied with tear gas and made mass arrests. The fighting lasted for 3 weeks, by which time the language ruling, later dropped, was no longer the main issue.

35 Johnny I hardly knew you

Irish

BRENDA PRINCE/FORMAT

Extract from a leaflet setting out UK war pensions and allowances. The figures are for 1986.

Gratuities for specified minor injuries

For the loss of	Officers	Other ranks	For the loss of	Officers	Other ranks
A. Fingers			**B. Toes**		
Index finger			Great toe		
More than 2 phalanges, including loss of whole finger	£3210	£3180	*through metatarso-phalangeal joint*	£3210	£3180
More than 1 phalanx but not more than 2 phalanges	£2570	£2545	*part, with some loss of bone*	£ 850	£ 845
1 phalanx or part thereof	£2140	£2120	1 other toe		
Guillotine amputation of tip without loss of bone	£1280	£1270	*through metatarso-phalangeal joint*	£ 850	£ 845
Middle finger			*part, with some loss of bone*	£ 430	£ 425
More than 2 phalanges, including loss of whole finger	£2780	£2755	2 toes, excluding great toe		
More than 1 phalanx but not more than 2 phalanges	£2140	£2120	*through metatarso-phalangeal joint*	£1280	£1270
1 phalanx or part thereof	£1710	£1695	*part, with some loss of bone*	£ 640	£ 635
Guillotine amputation of tip without loss of bone	£1070	£1060	3 toes, excluding great toe		
Ring or little finger			*through metatarso-phalangeal joint*	£1500	£1485
More than 2 phalanges, including loss of whole finger	£1710	£1695	*part, with some loss of bone*	£ 850	£ 845
More than 1 phalanx but not more than 2 phalanges	£1500	£1485	4 toes, excluding great toe		
1 phalanx or part thereof	£1280	£1270	*through metatarso-phalangeal joint*	£2140	£2120
Guillotine amputation of tip without loss of bone	£ 640	£ 635	*part, with some loss of bone*	£ 850	£ 845

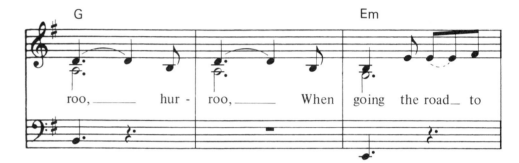

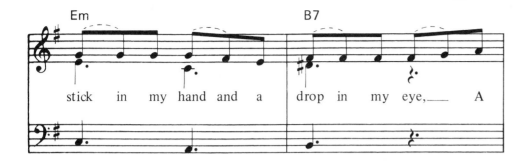

stick in my hand and a drop in my eye, ___ A

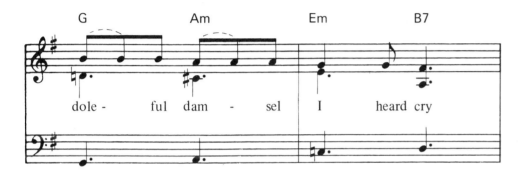

dole - ful dam - sel I heard cry

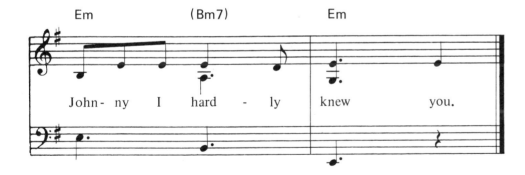

John- ny I hard - ly knew you.

The chord symbols are an alternative harmonisation which should not be played together with the piano arrangement.

2 Where are the legs with which you run,
    Hurroo, hurroo,
Where are the legs with which you run,
    Hurroo, hurroo,
Where are the legs with which you run
When you went to carry a gun?
Indeed your dancing days are done!
Johnny I hardly knew you.

3 Where are the eyes that looked so mild,
    Hurroo, hurroo,
Where are the eyes that looked so mild,
    Hurroo, hurroo,
Where are the eyes that looked so mild
When you my poor heart first beguiled?
And will you never see your child?
Johnny I hardly knew you.

4 You haven't an arm and you haven't a leg,
    Hurroo, hurroo,
You haven't an arm and you haven't a leg,
    Hurroo, hurroo,
You haven't an arm and you haven't a leg,
You're an eyeless, noseless, chickenless egg,
You'll have to be put in a bowl to beg.
Johnny I hardly knew you.

This very old Irish song was, with staggering irony, made into a recruiting song during the American War of Independence – 'When Johnny comes marching home'. It was revived in this form for World War 2.

36 The Rainbow Warrior

words: Patricia Middleton
music: Douglas Dimm

'When the earth is sick, the animals will begin to disappear. When that happens the Warriors of the Rainbow will come to save them.'

from a North American Indian prophecy

1 Long ago when the world was new
  The grass waved green and the sky was blue;
  The sun shone warm and the air was sweet,
  And the people all had food to eat.
  Then the Rainbow Warrior smiled to see
  That the earth was strong and the people free.

  Drum, drum, beat the drum,
  And the Rainbow Warrior, he will come.

2 Soon the pines grew tall and the hawk flew high,
  The cold moon glowed in the midnight sky;
  And the fishes swam in the silver stream,
  And the earth spun round in a timeless dream.
  Then the Rainbow Warrior smiled to see
  That the earth stayed strong and the people free.

  Drum, drum, beat the drum...

3 Then the white man came and his gun brought fear,
  He seized the land and he slew the deer;
  And he killed the braves and the widows cried,
  And without the hunters the children died.
  Then the Rainbow Warrior frowned; he saw
  That man would live in peace no more.

  Drum, drum, beat the drum...

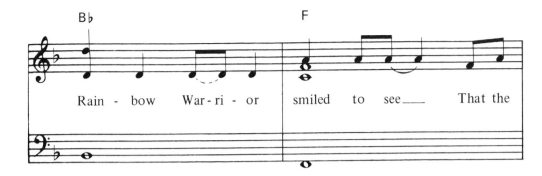

Rain - bow War - ri - or | smiled to see___ That the

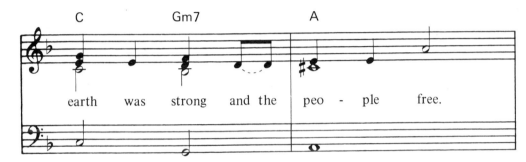

earth was strong and the | peo - ple free.

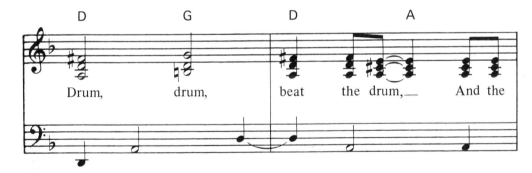

Drum, drum, | beat the drum,___ And the

Rain - bow War - ri - or, | he will come.

4 Next the white man laid the railroad down,
Where tepees stood there grew a town;
And he felled the trees and he trapped the bear,
And the homeless birds took to the air.
Then the Rainbow Warrior grieved to see
The earth grow sick and the creatures flee.

Drum, drum, beat the drum . . .

5 Last the factories rose, breathing flame and smoke;
Now the air grows thick and the cities choke;
And the giant tankers spill their waste
And the water now has a bitter taste.
Now the seabirds die upon the shore
And the great whale soon will be no more.

Drum, drum, beat the drum . . .

37 I come and stand at every door

words: Nazim Hikmet
music: traditional

1 I come and stand at every door,
   But none can hear my silent tread,
   I knock and yet remain unseen
   For I am dead, for I am dead.

2 I'm only seven although I died
   In Hiroshima long ago.
   I'm seven now as I was then.
   When children die, they do not grow.

3 My hair was scorched by swirling flame,
   My eyes grew dim and then were blind,
   Death came and turned my bones to dust
   And that was scattered by the wind.

4 I need no fruit, I need no rice,
   I need no sweets or even bread.
   I ask for nothing for myself
   For I am dead, for I am dead.

5 All that I ask is that for peace
   You fight today, you fight today –
   So that the children of the world
   May live and grow and laugh and play.

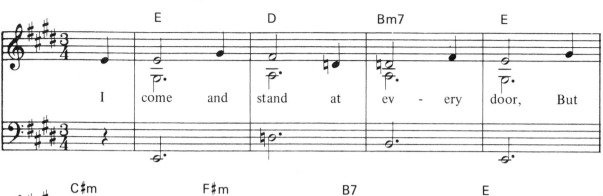

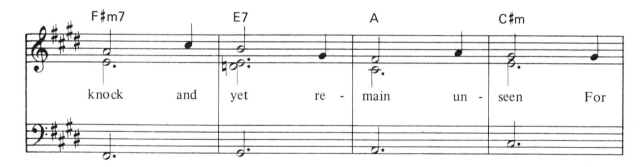

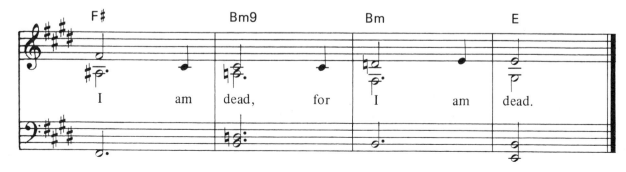

38 The hunting song

Tom Lehrer

39 The price

words: Peggy Aprahamian
music: David Chase

1 If an apple that's good costs in new pence
  The same as an apple that's not
  Why spend your money on bad fruit
  Why pay for the fruit that will rot?
  If a bullet that kills has a price tag
  The same as a book full of songs
  Why spend your money on bullets?
  Why pay for the pain and the wrongs?

2 If the price of defoliant equals
  The cost of the seed that you sow
  Why spend your money destroying
  The crop you intended to grow?
  If napalm that burns costs in money
  The same as the medicine that heals
  Why spend your money on napalm
  When you know how the burning feels?

  If a bomber can cost you in millions
  The price of a city you plan
  Why spend your money on bombers
  When it's houses you need for man?

3 If a submarine costs you in bank notes
  The same as more teachers and schools
  Why spend your cash on Polaris?
  Such spending is only for fools.
  If the cost of peace is equal
  To the cost of a wasteful war
  Why spend our money on killing
  When it's life that we're all here for?

'Non-violence is the answer to the crucial political and moral questions of our time: the need for man to overcome oppression and violence without resorting to oppression and violence.

Man must evolve for all human conflict a method which rejects revenge, aggression and retaliation. The foundation of such a method is love . . .

I refuse to accept the cynical notion that nation after nation must spiral down a militaristic stairway into the hell of nuclear destruction. I believe that unarmed truth and unconditional love will have the final word in reality.'

Martin Luther King: Speech accepting the Nobel Peace Prize (1964)

40 If you think with a bomb

Sydney Carter

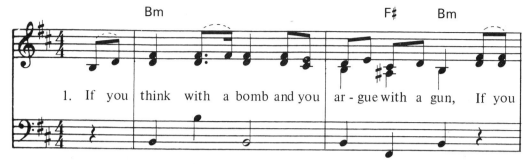

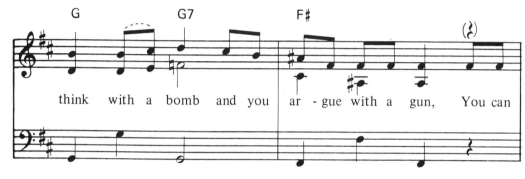

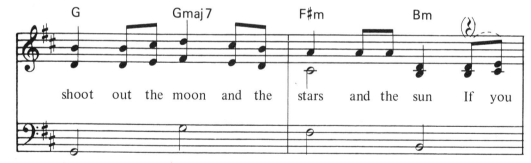

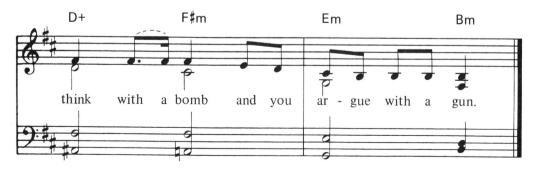

2 They rode through the town on a winter afternoon,
They rode through the town on a winter afternoon.
He shone like the sun and she shone like the moon
When they rode through the town on a winter afternoon.

3 They shot him down with a bullet from a gun,
They shot him down with a bullet from a gun.
There's blood on the moon and goodbye to the sun,
They shot him down with a bullet from a gun.

4 Oh, who can I blame for the sorrow and the shame?
Who can I blame for the sorrow and the shame?
Show me the target and tell me the name!
Who shall I blame for the sorrow and the shame?

5 My grief is a bomb and my sorrow is a gun,
My grief is a bomb and my sorrow is a gun.
Tell me, who can I kill for the deed that is done?
My grief is a bomb and my sorrow is a gun.

6 You think with a bomb and you argue with a gun,
You think with a bomb and you argue with a gun,
You can shoot out the moon and the stars and the sun,
If you think with a bomb and you argue with a gun.

A song which expresses opposing attitudes, verses 1 and 6 being gentle while verses 4 and 5 express bitterness and violence which are present to some degree in us all.

Sydney Carter sums up the song with the sentence 'If you answer one kind of violence by another, what do you get?' and says: 'This question, this song, was first prompted by the assassination of President Kennedy; though what has happened since in London, Belfast, Lebanon and Tripoli have kept it topical'.

41 The bonnie light horseman

English (19th century)

1. When Bo - ney com - man - ded his ar - mies to stand He le - velled his can - nons right o - ver the land. He le - velled his can - nons his vic - tory to gain, And he slew my light horse - man on the way com - ing home. Bro - ken heart - ed I'll wan - der, bro - ken - heart - ed I'll re - main Since my bon - nie light horse - man in the wars he was slain.

2 If I was a small bird and had wings to fly
I would fly o'er the salt sea where my love does lie
And with my fond wings I'd beat over his grave
And kiss the pale lips that lie cold in the clay.

Broken-hearted I'll wander . . .

3 The dove she laments for her mate as she flies –
Oh where, tell me where is my darling? she cries;
And where in this world is there one to compare
To my bonnie light horseman who was slain in the war?

Broken-hearted I'll wander . . .

42 Girls can do anything

Sandra Kerr

43 The sun is burning

Ian Campbell

1 The sun is burning in the sky.
   Strands of cloud are gently drifting by.
   In the park the dreamy bees
   Are droning in the flowers among the trees,
   And the sun burns in the sky.

2 Now the sun is in the west.
   Little kids lie down to take their rest.
   And the couples in the park
   Are holding hands and waiting for the dark,
   And the sun is in the west.

3 Now the sun is sinking low.
   Children playing know it's time to go.
   High above a spot appears,
   A little blossom blooms and then drops near,
   And the sun is sinking low.

4 Now the sun has come to earth
   Shrouded in a mushroom cloud of death.
   Death comes in a blinding flash
   Of hellish heat and leaves a smear of ash,
   And the sun has come to earth.

5 Now the sun has disappeared.
   All is darkness, anger, pain and fear.
   Twisted, sightless wrecks of men
   Go groping on their knees and cry in pain,
   And the sun has disappeared.

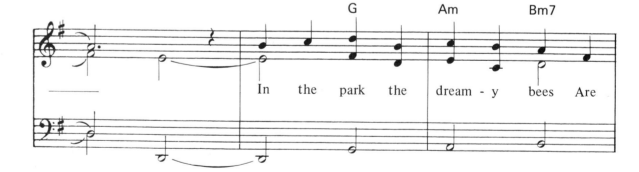

44 The peatbog soldiers

prison song

This song was written in Borger-moor concentration camp by the political prisoners of the Nazis. It was first performed in 1933 as part of a cultural event staged by the prisoners; they wanted to express their superiority over the brutish guards who had attacked their barracks. The performers sang with spades on their shoulders and the conductor's baton was a broken spade-handle. At the last chorus the prisoners drove their spades into the ground and left them sticking up like crosses on graves.

After this the song was kept for performance on special occasions and memorial days. It has since become widely known as a song of resistance, the words remaining close to the original but the tune having been adapted by several hands.

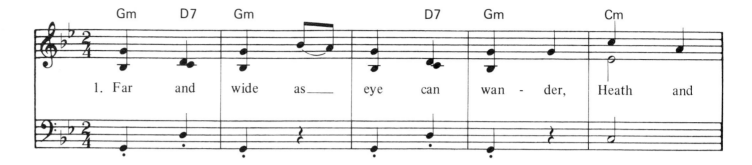

1. Far and wide as eye can wan-der, Heath and

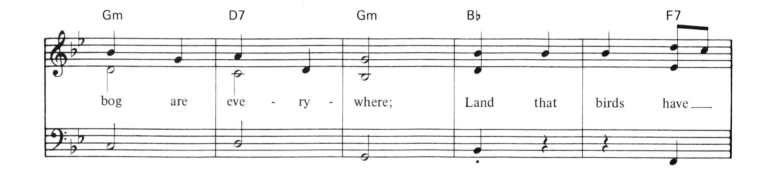

bog are eve-ry-where; Land that birds have long

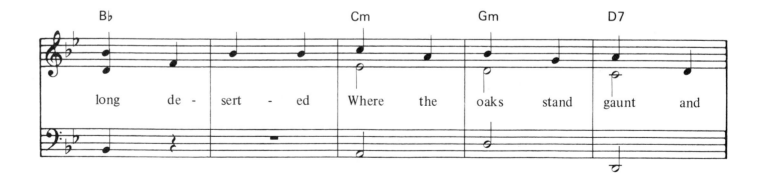

long de-sert-ed Where the oaks stand gaunt and

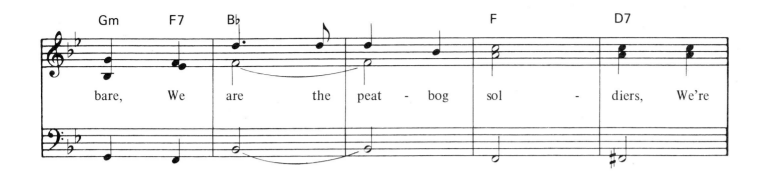

bare, We are the peat - bog sol - diers, We're

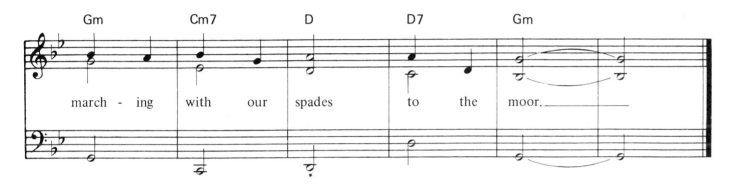

march - ing with our spades to the moor._____

2 Where the road would lead to freedom
Guns and barbed-wire greet our view;
Up and down the guards are pacing,
No-one, surely, can get through.

    We are the peatbog soldiers . . .

3 Yet for us there's no complaining,
Winter always leads to spring.
On the day we see our homeland
We will once more dance and sing.

    And then the peatbog soldiers
    Will march no more with spades
      to the moor.

Card sent from German Prisoner of War camp

Acknowledgements

The publishers would like to thank Leonora Davies, Martin Fautley, Andy Jackson, David Peacock and Janet Poynton for their help with the compilation of this book.

The following have kindly granted their permission for the reprinting of copyright songs:

Birmingham Sunday
© 1964 (unpub.), 1964, 1972 Silkie Music Publishers; all rights reserved including public performance for profit; used by permission.

Brother can you spare a dime
© 1932 Harms Inc, USA; Chappell Music Ltd, London W1Y 3FA; reproduced by permission of Chappell Music Ltd and International Music Publications.

Family secret
by permission of the composer.

Girls can do anything
by permission of the composer.

Glass of water
© 1967 Westminster Music Ltd, 19/20 Poland St, London W1V 3DD; for the territory of the World; used by permission; international copyright secured; all rights reserved.

History lesson
© 1964 EMI Music Publishing Ltd, London WC2H 0LD; reproduced by permission of EMI Music Publishing Ltd and International Music Publications.

The hunting song
by permission of the composer.

I come and stand at every door
by permission of Stormking Music Inc and Harmony Music Ltd, © 1963 Stormking Music Inc; international copyright secured; all rights reserved.

I remember Christmas
by permission of the composer.

If I was with a woman
by permission of Warner Bros Music Ltd, © Blackhill Music Ltd

If you think with a bomb
by permission of Stainer & Bell Ltd.

Jesus Christ was a man
by permission of Ludlow Music Inc, TRO Essex Music Ltd and Essex Music of Australia Pty Ltd; © 1957 TRO Essex Music Ltd.

Jute Mill song
music reproduced by permission of Belwin Mills Music Ltd.

Khayana
from *Folksongs of South Gujarat* by Madubhai Patel of Sarav, Gujarat.

Lullaby for a very new baby
by permission of the composer.

The maintenance engineer
by permission of the composer.

The mask I wore
by permission of Stainer & Bell Ltd.

The price
words by permission of Francis Aprahamian.

The Rainbow Warrior
words by permission of the author.

She's bought a hat like Princess Marina's
© 1969 Davray Music Ltd and Carlin Music Corp., 14 New Burlington St, London W1X 2LR, for the world.

The sun is burning
© 1963 TRO Essex Music Ltd, 19/20 Poland St, London W1; for the world; international copyright secured; used by permission; all rights reserved.

Turning the clock back
by permission of the composer.

In addition thanks are due to the following who have kindly granted permission for the use of text extracts:

The Controller of H.M.S.O. for permission to reproduce part of D.H.S.S. leaflet MPL 154 'Rates of war pensions and allowances'.

Robert Hamberger for the extract from *Journey to a birth*. The complete poem is published by Tom Bingham, 82 Dresden Close, Corby.

A. M. Heath & Co Ltd for the quotation from *The Road to Wigan Pier* by George Orwell.

Richards Literary Agency, New Zealand, for *Girls in a factory* by Denis Glover.

Robson Books Ltd for the passage from *Calling for Action* by Donald Soper.

The front cover photograph is by Andrew Wiard and is reproduced by permission of Report. It was taken at a demonstration in London against the Nationality Bill in April 1981. The back cover photograph and all the photographs within the book are reproduced by permission of Format Photographers. The postcard is reproduced by permission of Meregiliano-Nickol Collection.

Every effort has been made to trace and acknowledge copyright owners. If any right has been omitted, the publishers offer their apologies and will rectify this in subsequent editions following notification.

Though we travel the world over to find the beautiful,
we must carry it with us or we find it not

Ralph Waldo Emerson

museums, galleries, and sights information

Attraction

Address

Directions

Admission

Opening hours

Highlights

Attraction

Address

Directions

Admission

Opening hours

Highlights

Attraction

Address

Directions

Admission

Opening hours

Highlights

Attraction

Address

Directions

Admission

Opening hours

Highlights

restaurants, bars, and nightlife

restaurants, bars, and nightlife information

Name

Address

Telephone

Opening hours

Directions

Comments

Name

Address

Telephone

Opening hours

Directions

Comments

Name

Address

Telephone

Opening hours

Directions

Comments

Name

Address

Telephone

Opening hours

Directions

Comments

Name

Address

Telephone

Opening hours

Directions

Comments

Name

Address

Telephone

Opening hours

Directions

Comments

shops, stores, and markets

shops, stores, and markets information

Name

Address

Telephone

Opening hours

Purchases

Amount spent

Name

Address

Telephone

Opening hours

Purchases

Amount spent

Name

Address

Telephone

Opening hours

Purchases

Amount spent

Name

Address

Telephone

Opening hours

Purchases

Amount spent

Name

Address

Telephone

Opening hours

Purchases

Amount spent

Name

Address

Telephone

Opening hours

Purchases

Amount spent

journal

So it is in travelling; a man must carry knowledge with him, if he would bring home knowledge

Samuel Johnson

itinerary

Date

Destination

Depart

Arrive

Accommodations

Notes

Date

Destination

Depart

Arrive

Accommodations

Notes

Date

Destination

Depart

Arrive

Accommodations

Notes

Date

Destination

Depart

Arrive

Accommodations

Notes

museums, galleries, and sights

museums, galleries, and sights information

Attraction

Attraction

Address

Address

Directions

Directions

Admission

Admission

Opening hours

Opening hours

Highlights

Highlights

Attraction

Attraction

Address

Address

Directions

Directions

Admission

Admission

Opening hours

Opening hours

Highlights

Highlights

restaurants, bars, and nightlife

restaurants, bars, and nightlife information

Name

Address

Telephone

Opening hours

Directions

Comments

Name

Address

Telephone

Opening hours

Directions

Comments

Name

Address

Telephone

Opening hours

Directions

Comments

Name

Address

Telephone

Opening hours

Directions

Comments

Name

Address

Telephone

Opening hours

Directions

Comments

Name

Address

Telephone

Opening hours

Directions

Comments

shops, stores, and markets

shops, stores, and markets information

Name

Address

Telephone

Opening hours

Purchases

Amount spent

Name

Address

Telephone

Opening hours

Purchases

Amount spent

Name

Address

Telephone

Opening hours

Purchases

Amount spent

Name

Address

Telephone

Opening hours

Purchases

Amount spent

Name

Address

Telephone

Opening hours

Purchases

Amount spent

Name

Address

Telephone

Opening hours

Purchases

Amount spent

journal

One of the pleasantest things in the world is going a journey; but I like to go by myself

William Hazlitt

itinerary

Date _____

Destination _____
_____

Depart _____
_____

Arrive _____
_____

Accommodations _____
_____
_____

Notes _____
_____
_____
_____

Date _____

Destination _____
_____

Depart _____
_____

Arrive _____

Accommodations _____
_____

Notes _____
_____
_____
_____

Date _____

Destination _____
_____

Depart _____
_____

Arrive _____
_____

Accommodations _____
_____
_____

Notes _____
_____
_____

Date _____

Destination _____
_____

Depart _____
_____

Arrive _____

Accommodations _____
_____

Notes _____
_____
_____

museums, galleries, and sights

museums, galleries, and sights information

Attraction

Address

Directions

Admission

Opening hours

Highlights

Attraction

Address

Directions

Admission

Opening hours

Highlights

Attraction

Address

Directions

Admission

Opening hours

Highlights

Attraction

Address

Directions

Admission

Opening hours

Highlights

restaurants, bars, and nightlife

restaurants, bars, and nightlife information

Name

Address

Telephone

Opening hours

Directions

Comments

Name

Address

Telephone

Opening hours

Directions

Comments

Name

Address

Telephone

Opening hours

Directions

Comments

Name

Address

Telephone

Opening hours

Directions

Comments

Name

Address

Telephone

Opening hours

Directions

Comments

Name

Address

Telephone

Opening hours

Directions

Comments

shops, stores, and markets

shops, stores, and markets information

Name

Address

Telephone

Opening hours

Purchases

Amount spent

Name

Address

Telephone

Opening hours

Purchases

Amount spent

Name

Address

Telephone

Opening hours

Purchases

Amount spent

Name

Address

Telephone

Opening hours

Purchases

Amount spent

Name

Address

Telephone

Opening hours

Purchases

Amount spent

Name

Address

Telephone

Opening hours

Purchases

Amount spent

journal

The port from which I set out was, I think, that of the essential loneliness of my life

Henry James

itinerary

Date

Destination

Depart

Arrive

Accommodations

Notes

Date

Destination

Depart

Arrive

Accommodations

Notes

Date

Destination

Depart

Arrive

Accommodations

Notes

Date

Destination

Depart

Arrive

Accommodations

Notes

museums, galleries, and sights

museums, galleries, and sights information

Attraction

Attraction

Address

Address

Directions

Directions

Admission

Admission

Opening hours

Opening hours

Highlights

Highlights

Attraction

Attraction

Address

Address

Directions

Directions

Admission

Admission

Opening hours

Opening hours

Highlights

Highlights

restaurants, bars, and nightlife

restaurants, bars, and nightlife information

Name

Address

Telephone

Opening hours

Directions

Comments

Name

Address

Telephone

Opening hours

Directions

Comments

Name

Address

Telephone

Opening hours

Directions

Comments

Name

Address

Telephone

Opening hours

Directions

Comments

Name

Address

Telephone

Opening hours

Directions

Comments

Name

Address

Telephone

Opening hours

Directions

Comments

shops, stores, and markets

shops, stores, and markets information

Name

Address

Telephone

Opening hours

Purchases

Amount spent

Name

Address

Telephone

Opening hours

Purchases

Amount spent

Name

Address

Telephone

Opening hours

Purchases

Amount spent

Name

Address

Telephone

Opening hours

Purchases

Amount spent

Name

Address

Telephone

Opening hours

Purchases

Amount spent

Name

Address

Telephone

Opening hours

Purchases

Amount spent

journal

A traveller's chief aim should be to make men wiser and better

Jonathan Swift (*Gulliver's Travels*)

itinerary

Date _____ | Date _____

Destination _____ | Destination _____

Depart _____ | Depart _____

Arrive _____ | Arrive _____

Accommodations _____ | Accommodations _____

Notes _____ | Notes _____

Date _____ | Date _____

Destination _____ | Destination _____

Depart _____ | Depart _____

Arrive _____ | Arrive _____

Accommodations _____ | Accommodations _____

Notes _____ | Notes _____

museums, galleries, and sights

museums, galleries, and sights information

Attraction	Attraction
Address	Address
Directions	Directions
Admission	Admission
Opening hours	Opening hours
Highlights	Highlights
Attraction	Attraction
Address	Address
Directions	Directions
Admission	Admission
Opening hours	Opening hours
Highlights	Highlights

restaurants, bars, and nightlife

restaurants, bars, and nightlife information

Name

Address

Telephone

Opening hours

Directions

Comments

Name

Address

Telephone

Opening hours

Directions

Comments

Name

Address

Telephone

Opening hours

Directions

Comments

Name

Address

Telephone

Opening hours

Directions

Comments

Name

Address

Telephone

Opening hours

Directions

Comments

Name

Address

Telephone

Opening hours

Directions

Comments

shops, stores, and markets

shops, stores, and markets information

Name

Address

Telephone

Opening hours

Purchases

Amount spent

Name

Address

Telephone

Opening hours

Purchases

Amount spent

Name

Address

Telephone

Opening hours

Purchases

Amount spent

Name

Address

Telephone

Opening hours

Purchases

Amount spent

Name

Address

Telephone

Opening hours

Purchases

Amount spent

Name

Address

Telephone

Opening hours

Purchases

Amount spent

journal

*A man should know something of his own
country too, before he goes abroad*

Laurence Sterne

itinerary

Date _____ | Date _____

Destination _____ | Destination _____

Depart _____ | Depart _____

Arrive _____ | Arrive _____

Accommodations _____ | Accommodations _____

Notes _____ | Notes _____

Date _____ | Date _____

Destination _____ | Destination _____

Depart _____ | Depart _____

Arrive _____ | Arrive _____

Accommodations _____ | Accommodations _____

Notes _____ | Notes _____

museums, galleries, and sights

museums, galleries, and sights information

Attraction

Attraction

Address

Address

Directions

Directions

Admission

Admission

Opening hours

Opening hours

Highlights

Highlights

Attraction

Attraction

Address

Address

Directions

Directions

Admission

Admission

Opening hours

Opening hours

Highlights

Highlights

restaurants, bars, and nightlife

restaurants, bars, and nightlife information

Name

Address

Telephone

Opening hours

Directions

Comments

Name

Address

Telephone

Opening hours

Directions

Comments

Name

Address

Telephone

Opening hours

Directions

Comments

Name

Address

Telephone

Opening hours

Directions

Comments

Name

Address

Telephone

Opening hours

Directions

Comments

Name

Address

Telephone

Opening hours

Directions

Comments

shops, stores, and markets

shops, stores, and markets information

Name

Address

Telephone

Opening hours

Purchases

Amount spent

Name

Address

Telephone

Opening hours

Purchases

Amount spent

Name

Address

Telephone

Opening hours

Purchases

Amount spent

Name

Address

Telephone

Opening hours

Purchases

Amount spent

Name

Address

Telephone

Opening hours

Purchases

Amount spent

Name

Address

Telephone

Opening hours

Purchases

Amount spent

journal

It happen'd one day about noon going towards my boat, I was exceedingly surpriz'd with the print of a man's naked foot on the shore

Daniel Defoe (*Robinson Crusoe*)

clothing and shoe sizes

Women's dress sizes

US/Canada	6	8	10	12	14	16	18
Britain/Australia	8	10	12	14	16	18	20
Continental Europe/Asia	36/38	38/40	40/42	42/44	44/46	46/48	48/50

Women's shoe sizes

US/Canada/Australia	5	5½	6	6½	7	7½	8	8½	9	9½	10
Britain	3½	4	4½	5	5½	6	6½	7	7½	8	8½
Continental Europe/Asia	36	36½	37	38	38½	39	39½	40	41	42	42½

Men's suit sizes

US/Canada/Britain	34	35	36	37	38	39	40	41	42
Continental Europe/Asia	44	45	46	47	48	49	50	52	52
Australia	12	14	16	18	20	22	24	26	28

Men's collar sizes

US/Canada/Britain	14	14½	15	15½	16	16½	17	17½	18
Continental Europe/Australia/Asia	36	37	38	39	41	42	43	44	45

Men's shoe sizes

US/Canada	7	8	9	10	11	12	13
Britain/Australia	6	7	8	9	10	11	12
Continental Europe/Asia	40	41	42	43	44½	46	47

weights, measures, and temperatures

Length	Weight	Volume	°Fahrenheit	°Celsius
1 centimeter = 0.39 inches	1 gram = 0.04 ounces	10 milliliters = 0.34 fl. ounces	0	−18
1 meter = 3.28 feet	100 grams = 3.53 ounces	1 liter = 1.06 quarts	32	0
1 kilometer = 0.62 miles	1 kilogram = 2.2 pounds	1 liter = 0.26 gallons	41	5
8 kilometers = 5 miles			50	10
	1 ounce = 28.3 grams	1 teaspoon = 5 milliliters	59	15
1 inch = 2.54 centimeters	½ pound = 226 grams	1 tablespoon = 15 milliliters	68	20
1 foot = 30.48 centimeters	1 pound = 0.45 kilogram	1 fluid ounce = 30 milliliters	86	30
1 yard = 0.91 meters		1 cup = 237 milliliters	100	38
1 mile = 1.61 kilometers		1 pint = 473 milliliters	104	40
		1 quart = 0.95 liters		

world currencies, dialing codes, and time zones

Country	Currency	Dialing code	Time (hours) based on EST	Time (hours) based on GMT
Afghanistan	Afghani	+ 93	+9½	+4½
Albania	Lek	+ 355	+6	+1
Algeria	Algerian dinar	+ 213	+6	+1
Andorra	French franc, Spanish peseta	+ 376	+6	+1
Angola	Kwanza	+ 244	+6	+1
Antigua and Barbuda	East Caribbean dollar	+ 1268	+1	−4
Argentina	Peso	+ 54	+2	−3
Armenia	Dram	+ 374	+9	+4
Australia	Australian dollar	+ 61	+12 to +15 .	+7 to +10
Austria	Schilling	+ 43	+6	+1
Azerbaijan	Manat	+ 994	+10	+5
Bahamas	Bahamian dollar	+ 1242	EST	−5
Bahrain	Bahraini dinar	+ 973	+8	+3
Bangladesh	Taka	+ 880	+11	+6
Barbados	Barbadian dollar	+ 1246	+1	−4
Belarus	Belarusian rouble	+ 375	+7	+2
Belgium	Belgian franc	+ 32	+6	+1
Belize	Belizean dollar	+ 501	−1	−6
Benin	Central African franc	+ 229	+6	+1
Bermuda	Bermudian dollar	+ 1441	+1	−4
Bhutan	Ngultrum	+ 975	+11	+6
Bolivia	Boliviano	+ 591	+1	−4
Bosnia and Herzegovina	Dinar	+ 387	+6	+1
Botswana	Pula	+ 267	+7	+2
Brazil	Real	+ 55	+1 to +2	−3 to −4
Brunei	Bruneian dollar	+ 673	+13	+8
Bulgaria	Lev	+ 359	+7	+2
Burkina Faso	Central African franc	+ 226	+5	GMT
Burundi	Burundi franc	+ 257	+7	+2
Cambodia	Riel	+ 855	+12	+7
Cameroon	Central African franc	+ 237	+6	+1
Canada	Canadian dollar	+ 1	−3 to +1½	−3½ to −8
Central African Republic	Central African franc	+ 236	+6	+1
Chad	Central African franc	+ 235	+6	+1
Chile	Chilean peso	+ 56	+1	−4
China	Yuan	+ 86	+13	+8
Colombia	Colombian peso	+ 57	EST	−5
Congo	Central African franc	+ 242	+6	+1
Costa Rica	Costa Rican colón	+ 506	−1	−6
Croatia	Kuna	+ 385	+6	+1
Cuba	Cuban peso	+ 53	EST	−5
Cyprus	Cypriot pound, Turkish lira	+ 357	+7	+2
Czech Republic	Koruna	+ 420	+6	+1
Democratic Republic of Congo	New zaire	+ 243	+6	+1
Denmark	Danish krone	+ 45	+6	+1
Djibouti	Djiboutian franc	+ 253	+8	+3
Dominica	East Caribbean dollar	+ 1767	+1	−4
Dominican Republic	Peso	+ 1809	+1	−4
Ecuador	Sucre	+ 593	EST	−5
Egypt	Egyptian pound	+ 20	+7	+2
El Salvador	Colón	+ 503	−1	−6
Estonia	Kroon	+ 372	+7	+2
Ethiopia	Birr	+ 251	+8	+3
Fiji	Fiji dollar	+ 679	+17	+12
Finland	Markka	+ 358	+7	+2
France	French franc	+ 33	+6	+1
Gabon	Central African franc	+ 241	+6	+1
Gambia	Dalasi	+ 220	+5	GMT
Georgia	Lari	+ 995	+9	+4
Germany	Mark	+ 49	+6	+1

Country	Currency	Dialing code	Time (hours) based on EST	Time (hours) based on GMT
Ghana	Cedi	+ 233	+5	GMT
Greece	Drachma	+ 30	+7	+2
Greenland	Danish krone	+ 299	+1 to +4	−1 to −4
Grenada	East Caribbean dollar	+ 1473	+1	−4
Guatemala	Quetzal	+ 502	−1	−6
Guinea	Guinean franc	+ 224	+5	GMT
Guinea-Bissau	Central African franc	+ 245	+5	GMT
Guyana	Guyana dollar	+ 592	+1	−4
Haiti	Gourd	+ 509	EST	−5
Honduras	Lempira	+ 504	−1	−6
Hungary	Forint	+ 36	+6	+1
Iceland	Króna	+ 354	+5	GMT
India	Indian rupee	+ 91	+10$\frac{1}{2}$	+5$\frac{1}{2}$
Indonesia	Rupiah	+ 62	+12 to +13	+7 to +8
Iran	Rial	+ 98	+8$\frac{1}{2}$	+3$\frac{1}{2}$
Iraq	Iraqi dinar	+ 964	+8	+3
Ireland	Irish pound	+ 353	+5	GMT
Israel	Shekel	+ 972	+7	+2
Italy	Italian lira	+ 39	+6	+1
Ivory Coast	Central African franc	+ 225	+5	GMT
Jamaica	Jamaican dollar	+ 1876	EST	−5
Japan	Yen	+ 81	+14	+9
Jordan	Jordanian dollar	+ 962	+7	+2
Kazakhstan	Tenge	+ 7	+10 to +11	+5 to +6
Kenya	Kenya shilling	+ 254	+8	+3
Kuwait	Kuwaiti dinar	+ 965	+8	+3
Kyrgyzstan	Som	+ 996	+10	+5
Laos	Kip	+ 856	+12	+7
Latvia	Lats	+ 371	+7	+2
Lebanon	Lebanese pound	+ 961	+7	+2
Lesotho	Loti	+ 266	+7	+2
Liberia	Liberian dollar	+ 231	+5	GMT
Libya	Libyan dinar	+ 218	+6	+1
Leichtenstein	Swiss franc	+ 423	+6	+1
Lithuania	Litas	+ 370	+7	+2
Luxembourg	Luxembourg franc	+ 352	+6	+1
Macedonia	Denar	+ 389	+6	+1
Madagascar	Malagasy franc	+ 261	+8	+3
Malawi	Kwacha	+ 265	+7	+2
Malaysia	Ringgit	+ 60	+13	+8
Maldives	Rufiyaa	+ 960	+10	+5
Mali	Central African franc	+ 223	+5	GMT
Malta	Maltese lira	+ 356	+6	+1
Mauritania	Ouguiya	+ 222	+5	GMT
Mauritius	Mauritian rupee	+ 230	+9	+4
Mexico	Mexican peso	+ 52	−1 to −2	−6 to −7
Moldova	Leu	+ 373	+7	+2
Monaco	French franc	+ 377	+6	+1
Mongolia	Tugrik	+ 976	+13	+8
Morocco	Moroccan dirham	+ 212	+5	GMT
Mozambique	Metical	+ 258	+7	+2
Myanmar	Kyat	+ 95	+11$\frac{1}{2}$	+6$\frac{1}{2}$
Namibia	Namibian dollar	+ 264	+7	+2
Nepal	Nepalese rupee	+ 977	+10$\frac{3}{4}$	+5$\frac{3}{4}$
Netherlands	Netherlands guilder	+ 31	+6	+1
New Zealand	New Zealand dollar	+ 64	+17	+12
Nicaragua	Córdoba	+ 505	−1	−6
Niger	Central African franc	+ 227	+6	+1
Nigeria	Naira	+ 234	+6	+1
North Korea	Won	+ 850	+14	+9
Norway	Norwegian krone	+ 47	+6	+1
Oman	Omani rial	+ 968	+9	+4

Country	Currency	Dialing code	Time (hours) based on EST	Time (hours) based on GMT
Pakistan	Pakistani rupee	+ 92	+10	+5
Palau	US dollar	+ 680	+14	+9
Panama	Balboa	+ 507	EST	−5
Papua New Guinea	Kina	+ 675	+15	+10
Paraguay	Guaraní	+ 595	+1	−4
Peru	Nuevo sol	+ 51	EST	−5
Philippines	Philippine peso	+ 63	+13	+8
Poland	Zloty	+ 48	+6	+1
Portugal	Escudo	+ 351	+5	GMT
Puerto Rico	US dollar	+ 1787	+1	−4
Qatar	Qatari rial	+ 974	+8	+3
Romania	Leu	+ 40	+7	+2
Russian Federation	Ruble	+ 7	+7 to +17	+2 to +12
Rwanda	Rwandan franc	+ 250	+7	+2
St Kitts and Nevis	East Caribbean dollar	+ 1869	+1	−4
St Lucia	East Caribbean dollar	+ 1758	+1	−4
St Pierre and Miquelon	French franc	+ 508	+2	−3
St Vincent and the Grenadines	East Caribbean dollar	+ 1784	+1	−4
San Marino	Italian lira	+ 378	+6	+1
Saudi Arabia	Saudi riyal	+ 966	+8	+3
Senegal	Central African franc	+ 221	+5	GMT
Seychelles	Seychelles rupee	+ 248	+9	+4
Sierra Leone	Leone	+ 232	+5	GMT
Singapore	Singapore dollar	+ 65	+13	+8
Slovakia	Koruna	+ 421	+6	+1
Slovenia	Tolar	+ 386	+6	+1
Solomon Islands	Solomon Islands dollar	+ 677	+16	+11
Somalia	Somali shilling	+ 252	+8	+3
South Africa	Rand	+ 27	+7	+2
South Korea	Won	+ 82	+14	+9
Spain	Peseta	+ 34	+6	+1
Sri Lanka	Sri Lankan rupee	+ 94	+10½	+5½
Sudan	Sudanese pound	+ 249	+7	+2
Suriname	Suriname guilder	+ 597	+2	−3
Swaziland	Lilangeni	+ 268	+7	+2
Sweden	Swedish krona	+ 46	+6	+1
Switzerland	Swiss franc	+ 41	+6	+1
Syria	Syrian pound	+ 963	+7	+2
Taiwan	New Taiwan dollar	+ 886	+13	+8
Tajikistan	Tajik ruble	+ 7	+10	+5
Tanzania	Tanzanian shilling	+ 255	+8	+3
Thailand	Baht	+ 66	+12	+7
Togo	Central African franc	+ 228	+5	GMT
Tonga	Pa'anga	+ 676	+18	+13
Trinidad and Tobago	Trinidad and Tobago dollar	+ 1868	+1	−4
Tunisia	Tunisian dollar	+ 216	+6	+1
Turkey	Turkish lira	+ 90	+7	+2
Turkmenistan	Manat	+ 993	+10	+5
Uganda	Ugandan shilling	+ 256	+8	+3
Ukraine	Hryvna	+ 380	+7	+2
United Arab Emirates	Emirian dirham	+ 971	+9	+4
United Kingdom	Pound sterling	+ 44	+5	GMT
United States of America	US dollar	+ 1	EST to −5	−5 to −10
Uruguay	Uruguayan peso	+ 598	+2	−3
Uzbekistan	Som	+ 7	+10	+5
Venezuela	Bolivar	+ 58	+1	−4
Vietnam	Dong	+ 84	+12	+7
Western Samoa	Tala	+ 685	−6	−11
Yemen	Yemeni rial	+ 967	+8	+3
Yugoslavia	Yugoslav dinar	+ 381	+6	+1
Zambia	Kwacha	+ 260	+7	+2
Zimbabwe	Zimbabwean dollar	+ 263	+7	+2

First published in the United States in
2001 by Ryland Peters & Small, Inc.
519 Broadway
5th Floor
New York
NY 10012
Text, design, and photographs copyright
© Ryland Peters & Small 2001

10 9 8 7 6 5 4

ISBN 1 84172 217 0

Printed in China

Introduction by Caroline Brandenburger, former
editor of TRAVELLER magazine and editor of the
fifth and sixth editions of The Traveller's Handbook.

Photographs by Jan Baldwin, Catherine Brear,
Christopher Drake, Emilie Ekström, Scott Griffin,
Sarah Hepworth, Gabriella Le Grazie,
Brian Leonard, Robert Merrett, Andy Tough,
Simon Upton and Alan Williams.

Selected images from Waterside Living, Great
Escapes, Open Air Living and Wine Tastes Wine Styles,
all published by Ryland Peters & Small.